Balloons

by Miriam Sklar

No part of this publication can be reproduced in whole or in part, or stored in a retrieval system, or transmitted in any form or by any means, electronic, mechanical, photocopying, recording, or otherwise, without written permission of the publisher. For permission, write to Scholastic Inc., 557 Broadway, New York, NY 10012.

ISBN: 978-1-338-75068-3
Illustrated by John Lund
Copyright © 2021 by Miriam Sklar. All rights reserved.
Published by Scholastic Inc., 557 Broadway, New York, NY 10012

10 9 8 7 6 5 4 68 25 26 27/0

Printed in Jiaxing, China. First printing, January 2021.

There are long balloons.

There are round balloons.

There are big balloons.

There are high balloons.

There are dog balloons.

There are small balloons.

There are water balloons!